Side Launch

Side Launch

The Collingwood Shipyard Spectacle

by Robert Woodcock

SUMMERHILL PRESS
TORONTO

Cover: Oil painting by artist Marten Visser depicts the launch of
JOHN B. AIRD at Collingwood Shipyards on October 21, 1982.

Back Cover: Photograph by Rob McEwan shows PRAIRIE HARVEST
during her launch at Collingwood Shipyards on October 18, 1983.

Published by Summerhill Press Ltd.
Toronto, Ontario

Canadian Cataloguing in Publication Data
Woodcock, Robert, 1940 -
  Side Launch : the Collingwood Shipyard spectacle
ISBN 0-920197-00-0
1. Shipyards - Ontario - Collingwood - History.
2. Ships - Launching - History. I. Title
VM27.06W66 1984   623.83'09713'16   C84-098695-5

Distributed in Canada by:
Collier Macmillan Canada, Inc.
50 Gervais Drive
Don Mills, Ontario M3C 3K4

Printed in Canada

Acknowledgements

On the morning of November 6, 1981 the town of Collingwood was blasted by a cold gale-force wind. Waves of moisture-laden air swirled in all directions with a mean vengeance. It was not a day when one would expect to find Collingwood harbour lined with thousands of excited visitors. But they were there, defying the terrible weather, determined to witness another spectacular side ship launching.

I knew then that someone must examine and document why otherwise sane and rational people would endure such inconvenience to witness an event which lasts a mere 10 seconds.

I had identified the need but didn't possess adequate knowledge of the process to undertake such a challenge. To do so would require more than a desire supported by a dream. The first support I received in producing this book came from George Czerny of the Collingwood Enterprise-Bulletin newspaper. Then other people learned of my plans and generously provided much help. I will be forever grateful to the following who made it possible for me to complete this project: Algoma Central Railway (Marine Division); John H. Clarke of St. Clair, Michigan; Collingwood Chamber of Commerce; Joe B. Sheffer, Garry Cooke, G.A. Bert Van der Net, and the late W.A. Alex Webster all of the Collingwood Shipyards, a division of Canadian Shipbuilding and Engineering Limited; and special thanks to George Czerny and Fred McArthur of Collingwood Shipyards.

The Honourable John B. Aird (left) seated during post-launch luncheon ceremony with James R. Elder, President of Collship, and Mrs. Douglas A. Berlis, representing Algoma Central Railway.

FOREWORD

I am pleased to have been asked to write a brief foreword for Mr. Robert Woodcock's book entitled, "Side Launch — The Collingwood Shipyard Spectacle".

My life has been laced with many thrills but I must say that among the very greatest of thoroughly exciting days for me was the day that I stood on the bridge of the motor vessel JOHN B. AIRD and "rode her down" when she was side-launched at Collingwood.

I suppose it is a truism that a latent love of the sea belongs to many people. During the 1939/1945 War, I spent very nearly two years at sea on a Corvette and on a Frigate. Also, I became Chairman of the Algoma Central Railway which has a fine fleet of lakers, many of which were side-launched at Collingwood. As a result of these experiences, I am among those who have this special feeling for the sea, and for the men and the ships that sail upon it. As well, I believe my great hobby is my abiding interest in antique wooden launches which I continue to enjoy on the Muskoka Lakes.

Probably it can be said that side-launchings have become almost a lost art. There is no doubt that they take particular skills, sensitivity and great attention to detail. There is always present the element of risk to human life and when the ship hits the water without incident, a sigh of relief runs through the excited and colourful crowd. There is a spontaneous reaction of cheering, smiling and flag-waving. It is a time of celebration because, in reality, a new life has been created, one which will sail the Great Lakes and will be a credit to those who have created her.

Over the years, it has been one of my great pleasures to attend these side-launchings and to be associated with the people whose skill, devotion and love have created new ships.

In many ways, this special book is their message to you.

John B. Aird
Lieutenant Governor of Ontario

CONTENTS

1

CANADA'S AVALANCHE
OF STEEL

When Noah constructed his illustrious Ark many years ago he encountered a problem which continues to challenge modern-day builders of water-going vessels. This was finding a safe and practical method of transporting a large vessel, constructed on dry land, into its natural habitat — water. The solution can be very simple or highly complex depending upon the vessel's size, the style of building berth, and the characteristics of the water facilities. Noah's solution was unquestionably of a simplistic nature requiring only that his animal-laden Ark be allowed to float off its building supports as the floodwaters rose and the Ark became buoyant. We are all aware, and thankful, that Noah's launch plan was a success.

Thousands of water-going vessels have been constructed and launched since Noah's Ark, but the technique used by Noah to prepare for launching remains in use today by numerous shipyards around the world. However, because of the current scarcity of 40-day rains, the modern version of a float-launch normally takes place in an excavated site known as a *graving dock,* also known as a *dry dock*. When a ship is constructed in a graving dock the launch of the vessel is not very dramatic. It takes place by allowing water to slowly enter the graving dock until the vessel becomes water-borne and floats free of the keel blocks and other supports upon which it is built. Port Weller Dry Docks of St. Catharines, Ontario is an ideal example of a shipbuilding location which constructs and launches ships in a graving dock facility. But a trip to that shipbuilding site to witness a ship launch would not prove rewarding. To quote Alex Elliott, Senior Vice-President of Port Weller Dry Docks; ''Our launches are so passive it's not until the building berth timbers begin floating from beneath the hull that we know that the vessel has been launched.''

The construction and passive launch of a ship in a graving dock is obviously a safe and easily controlled process, but a substantial capital expenditure is required to construct such a shipbuilding facility. As well, during the period that a ship hull is under construction in a graving dock, that costly facility cannot be used for the purpose of undertaking repair contracts.

Port Weller Dry Docks facility, St. Catharines, Ontario.

The "unusual" side-launch of the LAKE FERNANDO at Buffalo Dry Dock Co. in 1919.

Because of the high cost of the graving dock facility, efficiency has determined that ships could be constructed at ground level and then launched into an adjacent water source after the hull is completed to the point where it is watertight. This has resulted in the evolution of two principal methods of transferring completed ship hulls from land to water: *end-launching* and *side-launching*. During end-launchings, usually from the stern or rear end, the ship slides into the water in a lengthwise movement. Side-launching, the most spectacular, requires the vessel to slide sideways with sufficient velocity to carry it free of the launch ramp and into an adjacent body of water. But many critical factors must be carefully considered when preparing a launch plan for the side-launching of a large vessel. Failure to do so can produce very embarrassing results. Such was the case when the steamer LAKE FERNANDO was side-launched in 1919 by the Buffalo Dry Dock Co. LAKE FERNANDO was not only side-launched, but was also launched onto her side. Not a desirable result!

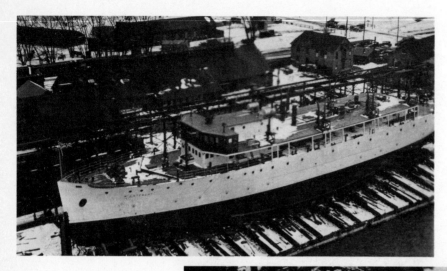

An unusual view of an unusual launching as the hydrographic steamer W.M. J. STEWART digs into the water so deeply during her launch on April 14, 1932 that she struck the basin's bottom and sustained damage to her bilge keel.

The side launching of the hydrographic steamer WM. J. STEWART on April 14, 1932 at Collingwood Shipyards was not executed in a desirable fashion either. With her aft end travelling down the launchways faster than the forward end, her stern entered the launching basin with such force that her bilge keel struck the basin's bottom. Only superficial damage occurred, but it was necessary to dry dock her to undertake necessary repairs.

End-launches would seem to be the least complicated of the two land-to-water launch methods, and be less likely to result in structural damage to the hull during launch. However, ship construction and launching of a ship hull from an end-launching ramp presents unique complications, and can place an enormous strain on the vessel's amidships location. During construction of any large ship hull which includes a plan for end-

14

launching, its keel is placed in a sloping position above launchways which angle toward the water source with sufficient
downward slope to enable gravitational forces to carry it into the
water during launching. To construct the hull in a level position
would require an enormous and impractical vertical stack of
packing timber (about 40 feet high at the stern end of a 1000-foot
ship). For this reason, large ship hulls which will be end-
launched are normally constructed on a building berth that has a
downward slope toward the water. Construction of a ship atop a
sloping building berth is very complicated as the off-level condi-
tion must be considered, and compensated for, during the entire
time the hull is under construction.

*Vessel atop sloping launch-
ways at the Harland and
Wolff Shipyards, Belfast,
Northern Ireland.*

15

End-launching of the ferry ST. DAVID at Harland and Wolff Shipyards, Belfast, Northern Ireland.

End-launchings are also restricted to water sources which are very deep, wide, and void of strong currents. Water depth is a critical factor as the lead end of the ship is forced to dive deeply into the water during launching. This happens because the lead end does not become buoyant until a substantial portion of the vessel has entered the water. That critical factor in an end-launching must be accurately determined and accounted for in the launch plan calculations to prevent severe stress on the hull's amidships section. These calculations can be severely affected by

16

the depth of the water above the launchways. Therefore, if tidal waters are a factor, accurate timing of the launch is also essential in order to meet the precise specifications of the launch plan.

Another major consideration is water currents such as those encountered in large rivers. Strong currents acting directly against the side of a ship hull as it enters the water stern-first during an end-launch can cause the vessel to twist sideways and create havoc with the launching cradle, the launchways, and the supporting timber.

Side-launching of LOUIS R. DAVIDSON in 1912 at Ashtabula, Ohio. One of the many inland shipbuilding sites in the Great Lakes region of North America in the 1800's.

These restrictions combined with the somewhat long run of water required to execute a successful end-launching created the need for an alternate ship launching method where either shallow, narrow, or fast flowing water sources existed. These conditions prevailed in many inland shipbuilding locations throughout Canada and the Great Lakes region of the United States during the 19th century. Side-launchings therefore evolved as the accepted and popular alternative to end-launchings throughout North America during that period of time. But as the number of shipyards decreased, and the size of the ships being constructed increased, the number of side-launching sites progressively diminished during the mid-1900's. This attrition continued to the point where Collingwood, Ontario, Canada is now the only remaining location in Canada where the unique art of side-launching of seaway-size ships is still practiced. This has made the Collingwood Shipyards a sacred location for the

18

Aerial views of Collingwood Shipyards in Collingwood, Ontario. It is the only remaining side-launching facility left in Canada where seaway-size vessels are built.

Crowds perch atop railcar adjacent to launch site at Collingwood Shipyards.

thousands of side-launch enthusiasts throughout North America. When launch days arrive, adults disappear from their places of work, and school children enthusiastically vacate their desks. Nothing can prevent them from attending another spectacular side ship launching at the Collingwood Shipyards where strangers and townspeople are drawn together at the launch site by an unexplained compelling force.

Upon arriving at the launch site spectators converse vibrantly, and by mid-morning conjecture runs wild among the first-time watchers. Typically, the large number of seasoned spectators contain the speculation with corrections of fact based on vivid and lasting memories of past side-launches. They willingly share their side-launch experiences as a demonstration of the profound bond which unites enthusiasts. As the crowd quickly grows in size during the moments prior to launch it becomes apparent that something special is about to happen. People of all ages, and from all walks of life are perched atop every accessible elevated structure within sight of the shipyards. Many spectators, some of whom have travelled for hours to reach the launch site are not aware that the spectacular incident which they are about to witness will last a mere ten seconds . . . but a dramatic ten seconds which will always be remembered by all who witness it.

20

The phenomenon of side ship launchings which occurs at the Collingwood Shipyards approximately twice each year is truly unique, and above all, dramatically spectacular. The event has no counterpart, therefore the intense human emotions experienced at a launching cannot be described in comparative terms. To fully appreciate the overwhelming nature of the emotions generated during the launching of a ship measuring over 700 feet in length, and towering 100 feet above ground, it is essential to actually witness the event. The reward . . . a feeling of amazement and awe that will linger in your mind forever.

The ships at Collingwood are constructed on a building berth which is perfectly level and holds the bottom of the hull about 6 feet above the ground. A narrow basin of water, which appears much too small to accommodate the launching of a large ship lies immediately adjacent to the building berth.

"Are they really going to launch that huge ship into that narrow basin?"

On launch day, 9000 tons of steel and water ballast (water pumped into the hull's forward ballast tanks to counterbalance the heavier aft end of the hull) stands poised on the building berth anxiously awaiting its spectacular side-slide and thunderous plunge into the narrow launching basin. This overwhelming scene is duplicated in very few locations in the world. Sturgeon Bay, Wisconsin and Gdansk, Poland are two other locations where side-launching facilities exist. However, the extremely narrow width of the launch basin in Collingwood presents an engineering challenge which make it the greatest of all locations. For this reason, the Collingwood Shipyards is considered "the side ship launching capital of the world" by all knowledgeable launch enthusiasts.

Many of the several thousand spectators who attend each side ship launching at Collingwood do so in appreciation of the skill and precise calculations required to safely transfer 9000 tons of weight sideways from an elevated position on dry land to a narrow basin of water measuring only 105 feet in width. The typical beam (width) of the ships constructed at Collingwood measure about 76 feet, leaving only 29 feet of spare basin space; an almost negligible margin considering the ship's weight and overall dimension. There's no room for error and there's no second chance. Once the ship is cut loose, gravity takes control of the 9000 tons of moving force. All pray that the calculations were correct. Otherwise . . . it's unthinkable!

Other spectators who have not had the opportunity to become familiar with the challenging "behind the scene" engineering aspects of launchings at Collingwood are still able to enjoy the spectacle by witnessing the physical elements which are readily apparent to even the most inexperienced observer. The obvious happenings, which demand one's attention and captivate all spectators, include an increasing level of anticipation prior to the moment of launch, followed by a thunderous roar of binding and clapping timber and a huge flood of water which rushes in all directions as the ship plunges sideways into the narrow launching basin.

Launch of the 639 foot HOSHELAGA on August 4th, 1949 brings Collingwood to a standstill. This was the author's first view of a side-launch at the age of 9.

When I became hooked on side-launchings in 1949, at the age of 9 when the mighty HOSCHELAGA was launched, it was these physical elements which captivated my sense of excitement. However, as my interest and knowledge of side-launchings expanded, I soon realized that it involved far more than a thunderous noise and rushing flood of water. My experience is typical of other enthusiasts who are first captivated

by the spectacle, but then develop an interest in the mechanics and engineering of side-launching.

For the freshman attending his first side-launching at Collingwood, the initial impression is; "are they actually going to launch that huge ship sideways into that tiny bit of water?" Even seasoned spectators have to wonder why the launching of such large ships in this way was ever undertaken.

2

COLLINGWOOD SHIPYARDS

The ships presently being constructed at Collingwood would dwarf the first steel-hull one built there, the HURONIC which measured only 321 feet long and 43 feet wide. It was launched on September 12, 1901, and represented not only the first steel hull ship constructed by the Collingwood Shipyards, but also the first by any Canadian shipyard. During that era the typical ship built at Collingwood was less than 400 feet in length and substantially lighter than present hulls. But while the size and weight of the ships have increased dramatically, the dimensions of the launching facilities at Collingwood have remained basically unchanged since 1901 when the HURONIC was side-launched. Consequently, the static size of the launching basin progressively placed greater demands on the team of officials and engineers responsible for the safe launching of their ships. But they have met the challenge and have become true professionals of the highly complex side-launch process.

The atmosphere of excitement which accompanied the side-launching of HURONIC also remains unchanged. For 83 years the spectacle of launching steel-hull vessels sideways at Collingwood has retained the ability to captivate the spectator.

The majestic vessel HURONIC, the first steel-hull vessel built at Collingwood Shipyards, is seen here in Collingwood harbour during what is believed to be her maiden voyage in 1902.

Launches of the ROYAL-TON at Collingwood on August 9th, 1924 (opposite page) and the COLLING-WOOD on October 5th, 1907.

Following the launching of HURONIC in 1901 the local newspaper reported that "several thousand intensely interested spectators had gathered to witness the event." Then 83 years later newspaper and television reports of the launching of PRAIRIE HARVEST on October 18, 1983 stated that "several thousand spectators stood in a state of awe while the PRAIRIE HARVEST took her first taste of Georgian Bay water."

But there have been changes to other aspects of the launchings since 1901, especially to the launch procedures that are followed. As an example, it is unlikely that with the present procedures they would have retained the original Launchmaster's signal to the axemen to cut the ship loose, that signal being the Launchmaster dropping his handkerchief to the ground.

During the earlier days of the shipyard the railroad played an important part in the construction and launching of Collingwood-built ships. Most of the steel and other material used during ship construction was transported to the site by steam trains. On launch day hundreds of officials and interested spectators from various cities would assemble in Toronto and board a special train destined for Collingwood. So significant was the train's arrival in Collingwood that the ship launchings would be timed to accomodate the train schedule. This resulted in one launch being delayed until 4:20 in the afternoon. That launch took place on May 22, 1913 when the 536-foot JAMES CARRUTHERS became the largest vessel built to that date at Collingwood.

The Collingwood Shipyards, which operates under the trade name Collship, employs up to 1000 tradesmen whose efforts and talents are collectively focused on each individual ship constructed. A substantial number of specialty trades are employed in the construction of ships and typically include: machinists, tinsmiths, pipefitters, engineers, stagers, carpenters, electri-

cians, designers, burners, welders, blacksmiths, engine fitters, painters, brake and punch operators, assemblers, chippers, riggers, crane operators, plumbers and joiners.

Possibly the single most important tradesmen in the ship-building process are the shipwrights.

Beginning with the strategic placement of the first prefabricated component of the vessel onto the building berth until the hull is completed and launched, the shipwrights oversee the hull's destiny. All launch preparations are coordinated through the shipwrights whose foreman is designated as the Launchmaster. He is responsible for the critical decision to cut the ship loose on launch day.

Prefabricated hull components, like pieces of a huge jigsaw puzzle, are hoisted into position atop the building berth where they are welded together to form another massive ship hull.

31

Precise installation and alignment of the ship's propeller and steering nozzle must take place before the ship enters the water on launch day.

When the Collingwood Shipyards hold consecutive orders for the purchase of their ships, the functions of keel laying, hull construction and launching represent a continuous cycle. Prefabricated hull components, each weighing up to 40 tons (the crane hoisting capacity will be increased to 120 tons in 1984), are constructed in the comfort of large buildings and then are transported by crane to the building berth where they are welded together to form the hull. Immediately following each launching the building berth is cleared of all launch timber and equipment

Laying of the keel and accompanying ceremony at Collingwood Shipyards for Hull No. 227, later to become the M/V PRAIRIE HARVEST.

and the shipwrights prepare for placement of the first prefabricated component of another hull. This function is called the *keel laying* and receives ceremonial recognition. The keel laying represents the first of three special events in the creation of ships; the other two being the *launchings* and the *sea trials*. The launchings are the most spectacular and dramatic of the two events, however, the sea trials represent the final test of the shipyard's ability to construct high quality vessels. The Collingwood Shipyards is renowned for excellence and efficient workmanship. It is for this reason that it has continued to survive and progress while many other shipyards throughout the world have ceased to operate. The thousands of spectators who enjoy the spectacular launch of each ship created at Collingwood are collectively hoping this success continues to enable the side-launch method to remain as a lasting Canadian institution.

3

LAUNCH PREPARATIONS BEGIN

The actual launch takes a mere ten seconds, however, the preparation for launch requires the undertaking of numerous detailed tasks which begin approximately three months prior to launch day and consume over 16,000 man hours. Another 2000 hours are required for cleaning up after a launch. It is necessary for each ship hull to be separately analyzed for its particular weight and dimensions when developing a complete launch plan, but much of the planning is based on knowledge garnered from past launches. It would be impossible to accomplish the launchings presently performed at Collingwood without the benefit of past experience. Knowledge is passed down from seasoned side ship launching veterans and has been progressively refined to the point where a seemingly impossible task is accomplished in an almost routine manner. The qualification of "almost" is applicable because there is always some degree of justified apprehension by the team responsible for the launchings. With the knowledge that 9000 tons of weight will be unleashed to the grasp of gravitational forces at launch moment, only a fool would offer an unqualified guarantee of total success.

Completed hull sitting in level position on the building berth at Collingwood Shipyards.

The launch process commences when the shipwrights begin placing huge launch timbers, known as *launchways*, beneath the ship hull when it nears completion. These wooden launchways measure up to 80 feet in length, are 24 inches wide and 15 inches deep. Until the late 1970's the launchways were constructed from a solid piece of Oregon Fir wood. However, because of the dwindling availability and considerable cost (about $7000 each in 1983) of such large timbers, replacement launchways are of a laminated construction which are only about $5000 each. In addition to costing less, the laminated launchways have proven to be stronger than those made from a solid piece of timber.

The huge wooden launchways must be positioned beneath the ship hull at precise right angles to the hull's length. They are spaced so that there are about 47 launchways from bow to stern of the vessel. Each launchway is supported by an array of wooden block packing placed beneath the launchways in such a manner to provide a downslope of 1-1/8 inches per foot of launchway. This results in a decline of about 8 feet over the full length of each launchway. That degree of declivity, which has proven to be ideal for the side-launching of most ship hulls, must be precisely consistent for all 47 launchways forming the launch ramp. Otherwise, the *packing timber*, which is later placed between the launchways and the ship's bottom, would not maintain a consistent compression on all 47 launchways during the critical slide at launch time. Any deviation from this requirement would place an enormous strain on the hull's bottom at the

One of the huge launch timbers measuring 2 feet in diameter.

location of any high spots along the launch ramp. The skill of a seasoned shipwright is required to ensure precise placement of the launchways in order to meet the exacting requirements of a side ship launching.

When the launchways have been properly positioned and supported from beneath, U-shaped slides known as *butterboards* are placed atop each launchway in an inverted position. Because all material atop the launchways will be launched, this includes packing timbers as well as the ship hull, a lubricating method must be employed between the launchways and the butterboards. The lubricant is applied to the launchways and butterboards in two layers, each about 3/16'' thick when compressed. The base coat consists of a solid wax base and is heated to a temperature of about 200°F at which point it liquifies and is applied with small hand swabs. When the base coat has solidified, a layer of soap-based lubricant is applied by hand (rubber gloves, face shields and aprons are used to protect the workers) and forms the slip-coat. The lubricants used to minimize friction between the launchways and butterboards have been refined considerably since the Collingwood Shipyards first began launching steel-hull vessels in 1901. The composition of present lubricants varies substantially from the beef tallow originally considered the ideal lubricant. Other bizarre lubricants such as rotten bananas have been used at other shipyards, and if you've ever "launched" yourself on a banana peel you'll understand why they would work for ships.

Lineup of 47 lubricated launchways beneath the M/V LAKE WABUSH.

The present combination of lubricants was developed at Collingwood for the launching of ALGOWOOD on October 7, 1980. That ship was cut loose on schedule at 11:45 a.m., however it sat stubbornly glued to the launchways for 14 agonizing minutes before finally giving way to the forces of gravity. When the slide did commence the hull slid diagonally down the launch ramp in a frightening manner with the forward end leading the stern by several feet. That type of uneven side-launch, if sufficiently severe, can cause structural damage to the hull. In an effort to prevent a reoccurance of such hang-ups, various combinations of lubricants were subsequently tested on a launchway assembly designed to simulate actual launch conditions. After 200 hours of testing, the Keystone lubricant compositions were developed for the launch of LAKE WABUSH and worked perfectly. When the 20 triggers were activated to release that ship hull at 11:45 a.m. on April 28, 1981, it appeared to leap into the launch basin.

The butterboards, which are totally dependent on the lubricants in order to function, are composed of several individual sections, each 8 feet in length. The sections are laid end-to-end atop the launchways, with a small space separating each section, and are attached together on each side by metal straps.

Cross section diagram of a vessel sitting on building berth at Collingwood Shipyards.
A. Chain to drag box
B. Trigger mechanism cable
C. Chopping block
D. 100-ton hydraulic jack
E. Trigger shore
F. Butterboards
G. Wedges
H. Launchways
I. Launching basin

This sectioned arrangement of butterboards provides a flexible but continuous sliding medium for the full length of each launchway. Post-launch retrieval of the butterboards from the launching basin is also simplified as well. The strips of butterboard sections, about 72 feet in length, are held in place atop the launchways by large staple-like cleat devices known as *dogs*. Four dogs are used on each launchway/butterboard assembly: two at the top end which are installed just prior to launch day, and another two at the lower end of the launchways which are removed just prior to launch day, leaving the *top dogs* to help hold the vessel in position.

When the butterboards are properly positioned and secured, an intriguing process known as *packing* begins. The large wedge-shaped space between the top of the butterboards and bottom of the ship hull (eight feet high at the low end of the launch ramp) must be packed with about 250,000 board feet of timber to carry the weight of the ship on launch day. The packing consists of timbers which are 10" x 12" in diameter and 10 feet in length. Two rows of these timbers running side-by-side are required atop each 32-inch wide butterboard assembly. A sufficient number of tiers are applied until the entire triangular

Side view of the arrangement of packing timbers underneath the ship's hull.

39

Hardwood wedges being placed between tiers of planking.

space between the butterboards and the ship's bottom is packed. The top of the packing must mate precisely with the ship's contours from side to side, including the extreme bow and stern sections where it is necessary to prepare and fit customized blocking in a saddle fashion. Each tier of packing plank is separated by pieces of smaller timbers which are placed at right angles to the larger planking and the launchways. At a convenient height in the packing timber, hardwood wedges are placed between two tiers of planking for the full length and on both sides of the 47 launchway assemblies. The wedges are 3 inches square at the heavy end and measure 16 inches in length. They are spaced about 3 inches apart, except for the bow and stern areas where the spacing is about 2 inches to compensate for the more narrow hull size at the centre keel line. This spacing arrangement requires the use of nearly 10,000 wedges throughout the packing. Each wedge will be required to lift almost one ton of the vessel's weight on launch morning.

At strategic locations along the length of the launch ramp, 20 launchways are chosen for the installation of trigger mechanisms which are used to release the ship's weight to the forces of gravity. Each *trigger* launchway is firmly secured in position by four large poles of spruce shoring. Two shores are located on each side of the trigger launchways. The shores are positioned parallel to the launchways and slope towards the ground at an angle of about 20 degrees. The top ends are placed against large wooden *cudgel blocks* which have been securely bolted to the launchways. The shore bottoms are then packed tight against either the concrete keel-block footing running beneath the hull's centre line or the launching basin's retaining wall. The 20 trigger launchways secured by the 80 large dog shores will hold the ship hull in a controlled position between the time its weight is transferred to the launchways and the dramatic release of the ship at launch moment.

The trigger mechanisms represent one of the most critical devices used in the side ship launching process. Each must be sufficiently strong to withstand over 40 tons of shear force while also being able to instantly release those same forces in a controlled manner at a critical moment. To accomplish this important procedure, the trigger mechanisms employ a combination of materials consisting of wood, steel and manila rope. Each of these materials, which have distinct and differing properties, are used in a manner which exploits their particular characteristics.

Overhead view of ship and launching basin at Collingwood Shipyards.
A. Triggers
B. 15 drag boxes
C. Launchmaster's platform
D. Launchways
E. Wave deflector
F. Viewing platform
G. Launching basin

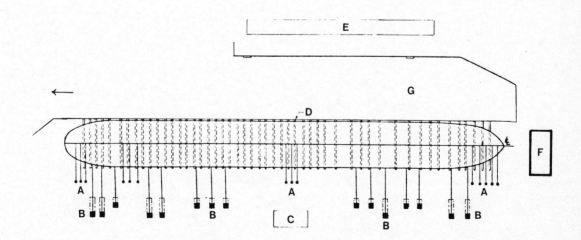

One of 20 trigger mechanisms consisting of a wooden timber, a steel I-beam, wire cable, and a length of manila rope.

When the trigger launchways are securely in place, the trigger mechanisms are assembled with precision and considerable care. Each trigger consists of a wooden timber, a steel I-beam, several feet of wire rope, and a length of manila rope. The steel I-beam, about 7 feet in length, is placed horizontal and at a right angle to its respective launchway with one end resting against a cudgel block's upper end. A piece of oak timber measuring 12 x 12 inches and about 5 feet long, representing the actual trigger device, is then positioned in the trigger arrangement at a sloping angle of about 30 degrees to the horizontal. The bottom end is placed against the steel I-beam at a distance of about 18 inches out from the launchway. The top end is then pressurized in position against a heavy lug which is welded to the ship's bottom. In order to secure the trigger arrangement in place until final launch routines are performed, a cable is positioned near the outer end of the steel I-beam to act as a lever. The cable is then attached to the ship's bottom and drawn taut by the use of a turnbuckle. The I-beam lever and the 5-foot-long wooden trigger timber are now held in position by the taut cable.

The mechanism to shift the ship's weight to the launchways on launch morning, while maintaining complete control until launchtime, is now in place. No additional significant prelaunch procedures are required until just prior to launch day.

42

4

COUNTDOWN TO LAUNCH

During the last few working days prior to launch day a series of firmly established routines are followed which will bring all normal activities within the shipyard to a complete halt about one hour prior to launch. The ship must be free of all obstructions or attachments in the launch path, therefore all scaffolding, ladders, walkway ramps, and power source lines such as air pressure and electricity feeds are disconnected from the vessel and stored until the post-launch phase of construction. As well, all moveable objects must be either removed from the ship or be securely lashed down. During a side-launch any loose objects aboard ship will become flying missiles when it comes to a stop at the end of its plunge into the launching basin. During the launch of the ALGOBAY on June 19, 1978, an unscheduled demonstration of the need to secure all loose objects took place when the huge ship jerked to a sudden stop minus one hatch cover, weighing over six tons, which was hurled off the deck. Fortunately the hatch cover landed near the ship's stern and into the water. It was subsequently salvaged from the harbour bottom by divers, and while no damage occured, the incident clearly demonstrated the need to anticipate all possible complications which may occur during a launch.

*Last minute cleanup on the
day before launch. All elec-
trical lines, scaffolding and
ramps are dismantled.*

44

Beneath the hull, final launch preparation procedures and adjustments are taking place. The temporary cables and turnbuckles holding the 20 trigger mechanisms in position are replaced by an arrangement of wire ropes and two sizes of manila rope. A heavy wire cable is looped around and secured within the grooved outer end of each steel trigger lever.

The 20 cables, running at right angles to the ship's length, extend from beneath the hull out past the inboard side of the launch ramp. Several feet beyond that point they will be secured by lengths of thick manila rope and a steel cable tackle arrangement which is anchored to the solid foundation of a crane track. Several loops of 5/8 inch manila rope are used to unite each wire cable with its restraining tackle. The loops of rope lie atop wooden chopping blocks, and all will be cut simultaneously with razor-sharp axes to release the triggers at launch moment. In the interim all exposed manila rope is carefully covered with plastic sheeting to protect it from moisture which would alter the precise amount of tension existing when the trigger arrangements were pressurized. Each of the 20 triggers are designed to withstand in excess of 40 tons of hull weight, however, because of the leverage effect provided by the steel I-beam trigger lever, only about five tons of force is exerted on each restraining cable and tackle system.

A view of the trigger mechanism from underneath the hull.

The design of the trigger arrangements is critical for a successful side-launch, but the Collingwood Shipyards must also respond to another major engineering challenge; how to stop the raging mass of weight from striking the far side of the launching basin wall during launch. To account for this the design department must calculate the exact projected path which the ship will travel when it roars sideways down the launchways. There is no room for error!

These calculations are used to determine the strategic placement of 18 *drag boxes* (the actual number is determined by the weight of each individual vessel) along the inboard side of the launch ramp area. Each drag box weighs in excess of 25 tons and consists of various pieces of scrap metal inside the steel drag box. The drag boxes are connected to the ship at the *launch lugs*, steel loops which are welded to the inboard side of the ship. The lugs must withstand an enormous strain when the ship meets the end of its launch path. To enable the vessel's side to withstand these

On page opposite, tackle restraining system anchored to crane track foundation (top), and the plastic covered manila rope lying on top of the chopping block (bottom).

Drag boxes, weighing in excess of 25 tons each are spaced in precise position along the inboard side of the ship.

47

Eight of the 18 drag chains hanging from the inboard side of PRAIRIE HARVEST.

severe stresses, the lugs extend into the ship where a continuous weld unites them to webbing which joins the skin with the inner wall of the hull. This creates a firm anchor for the lugs. Eighteen huge *stud-link chains*, measuring an average of 140 feet in length and weighing over 10 tons each are then used to connect the drag boxes to the lugs. Between the combined weight of the 18 drag chains and boxes, over 600 tons of weight will act as a brake to prevent the ship from striking the east wall of the launching basin.

One huge link in the long chain of events leading towards a successful launch.

48

On June 7, 1958 at River Rouge, Michigan, EDMUND FITZ-GERALD was side-launched into a basin about 150 feet wide, substantially wider than Collingwood's 105-foot wide launching basin. To break the slide of the EDMUND FITZGERALD during her launch, large tether ropes were attached to her side and then anchored to land. This technique differs substantially from the chain and drag box method used at Collingwood. Calculations in the EDMUND FITZGERALD launch plan allowed for a maximum stretch of 25 per cent throughout the length of each rope. When the vessel was launched, the 25 per cent allowance was exceeded, causing the vessel to come perilously close to striking the launching basin wall. No collision or damage occurred, however this lesson clearly demonstrated the need for improved methods of breaking the slide of ships.

The ill-fated EDMUND FITZGERALD on launch day at River Rouge, Michigan.

Launchmaster for PRAIRIE HARVEST, Gordon Thomas (centre) goes over last minute launch plans with G.A. Van der Net (left) and Garry Cooke of the design team.

While the Collingwood Shipyards has found the stud-link chain and drag box techinique to be a reliable method for braking, considerable care and skill is exercised to ensure absolute success. Precise positioning of the drag boxes is essential and forms a critical element of the design department's documented launch plan. As an example, the design department has been known to have the position of the drag boxes adjusted by as little as 6 inches just prior to launch day as a part of the fine-tuning process. They must be arranged in a layout which will enable them to progressively check the ship's thrust and ultimately bring it to a complete halt at a precisely pre-determined point. The technique of progressive activation of the drag boxes was first used at Collingwood Shipyards during the launching of B.A. PEERLESS on July 28, 1952.

View of B.A. PEERLESS at the top of Hurontario Street in Collingwood in 1952 (top), and the subsequent launch in bottom photograph.

51

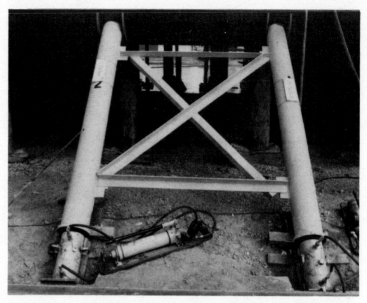

One of 4 two-jack units in position against bilge-line of PRAIRIE HARVEST (left), and one of the new 200-ton insurance jacks first used during the launch of ATLANTIC SUPERIOR (right).

Conspicuously standing out along the inboard side of the ship are eight bright-yellow steel shores. These rest against the ship's inboard *bilge line* (curvature where the side and bottom of the hull meet), and are held up from beneath by eight 100-ton capacity hydraulic jacks. The eight heavy gauge steel shores are paired together by metal cross-members which are welded to the shores to form four separate units. The units are spaced equally along the entire length of the vessel. Two additional 200-ton capacity jacks augment the eight 100-ton jacks whenever launch plan calculations indicate that they may be required for heavier hulls, such as was the case for No. 222 ATLANTIC SUPERIOR and No. 227 PRAIRIE HARVEST. It is probable however that the two 200-ton jacks will be installed as a precaution for all future launches. As Launchmaster Fred McArthur reasons; "I'd rather have the two insurance jacks in position than sitting in a storage shed if the ship won't move when we cut it loose." The base of each jack is wedged against a concrete crane track footing and the top ends are pressurized against the hull's bilge line where they are stabilized in position by lugs welded to the hull.

Starting with the spectacular launch of hull No. 222 on November 9, 1981, a system using *launch-time markers* was developed to calculate the ship's acceleration from a standing start as it moves down the launchways. The acceleration statistics gathered from each launch are then used in the development of subsequent launch plans. The launch-time

52

markers system consists of several wooden pickets stratigically spaced and fastened in a vertical position to the last launchway at the harbour end of the launch ramp. The pickets are painted white to contrast with the dark colour of the ship hull. At launch time a movie camera will be focused at the launch-time marker pickets from a position across the harbour. As the ship travels down the launch ramp, its stern stem will progressively strike each picket and cause them to fall over. The elapsed time frame between each strike provides the means to calculate the ship's acceleration and speed during launch.

When a ship is side-launched it is necessary to have the forward and aft ends move at precisely the same time and speed. Otherwise, the ship will fall off the launch ramp diagonally, increasing the damage to the launchways and packing timber. There is also a possibility of damage to the hull if severe binding or twisting takes place while travelling down the launchways. To minimize the danger of diagonal movement, a large quantity of water, about 1500 tons, is pumped into the forward ballast tanks to bring the vessel's forward-end weight into approximate balance with the aft end, which of course is the heaviest end of the ship. The water ballast is a simple yet practical means of bringing the weight of both ends of the vessel into approximate balance in order to ensure a geometrical launch of the ship.

Launch-time marker system in place at the stern of PRAIRIE HARVEST.

During the final two days prior to launch morning the Launchmaster meets with the various foremen and superintendents who are responsible for assigned launch tasks. Areas of responsibility are carefully reviewed to ensure a precise and safe execution of the launch plan. Perfection is not an option; it's part of the launch plan and typifies the Collingwood Shipyards' desire to attain excellence. More than 200 steel ship hulls have been successfully side-launched since 1901. During that time only one accident occurred. That was on May 29, 1969 when hull No. 192 TADOUSSAC broke loose from its secured position atop the launch ramp, causing havoc at the launch site. The cause of the accident was determined and equipment adjustments have since been made to prevent a reoccurance. That unfortunate incident serves as a lasting reminder that side-launching is a demanding process requiring considerable care.

All pre-launch preparations are completed and the ship awaits its destiny.

5

SPECTATORS CONVERGE
LIKE MIGRATING BIRDS

Spectators begin gathering early along the harbour's shoreline adjacent to the launching basin at Collingwood.

The thousands of spectators who have been awaiting launch day grow anxious as that special time approaches and final plans are made to travel hundreds of miles to witness "Canada's Spectacular Avalanche of Steel."

The normal launch time is 11:45 a.m., however, by early morning on launch day cars and buses with out-of-town plates begin appearing on the streets of Collingwood. They're all heading in the direction of the launch site like a flock of migrating birds, controlled by instinct.

Collingwood is a popular four-season tourist town, but the fact that ship launchings occur on work days make the presence of large numbers of tourists a conspicuous sight on an "off day". Conspicuous maybe. But out of place? Not in the least! They're part of the growing numbers of side-launch enthusiasts who travel to Collingwood from all across Canada and the United States for each spectacular launching. And why would otherwise sane people take up to two days off work, keep their children out of school and travel for hours to witness an industrial event which lasts a mere ten seconds?

56

There is no identifiable reason. Some return to view the launchings from a new spot each time because it's not possible to capture all the motion and excitement from any one vantage point. Others return to satisfy a haunting suspicion that some of the many elements believed to have been witnessed during previous side-launches, which are compressed into a ten-second glimpse of time, just didn't happen. Eventually, after viewing several launches, they learn to appreciate the fact that many spectacular happenings do occur simultaneously during a launching.

But how can anyone rationally explain the fact that most spectators are unable to provide a specific explanation for their habit of returning to every launch? Is there some compelling force pulling them towards the launch site? Or does their habit represent a unique phenomenon which may never be understood?

Collingwood Shipyards demonstrates its appreciation with this float in parade during Collingwood's 125th Anniversary celebrations.

Larry Beaton of Ottawa, Ontario is a side-launch enthusiast who readily admits to being affected by the spectacle in a way which no other event in his life has equalled. Larry spends seven hours driving from Ottawa to the launch site in Collingwood to experience ten seconds of emotional ecstasy. His devotion to the spectacle would be considered abnormal by anyone who has never witnessed the side-launching of a 9000 ton mountain of steel. However, thousands of seasoned enthusiasts undertake similar journeys to each launch. This phenomenal reaction is not limited to Canadians. Many citizens of the United States also travel to each launch regardless of weather conditions. The most noteworthy example is an organized group with headquarters located in Port Huron, Michigan. This organization, founded by Frank Crevier of Algonac, Michigan, is officially known as The Great Lakes Society for the Preservation of Side Ship Launching (T.G.L.S.F.T.P.O.S.S.L.), and has an active membership of hundreds of side-launch fans. These members attend each side-launching in Collingwood as part of a two-day excursion. Some travel to the launch by chartered bus and the remainder in private automobiles. They come from places like Sandusky and Toledo, Ohio; St. Clair and Marine City, Michigan; and of course, Port Huron, Michigan, headquarters of T.G.L.S.F.T.P.O.S.S.L.

Their excursion begins on the morning prior to launch day and includes a leisurely all day journey to Collingwood where they arrive and prepare for a highly enjoyable evening dinner meeting. The meetings are held in conclave and admittance is restricted to members of the organization and selected guests who are normally officials of the Collingwood Shipyards. The shipyard representatives show shipbuilding and launch movies, and provide answers to questions about the launch to be held the next morning. The meetings are partly a social event, but also reinforce the real purpose of the society. Their cause is specific and complies with the message of "preservation" deliberately conveyed in the society's depictive name. Recognizing that the Collingwood Shipyards is the only remaining side-launch location in Canada where seaway-size Great Lakes ships are side-launched, the society actively encourages the continuance of the spectacle.

The author's certificate of membership to the T.G.L.S.F.T.P.O.S.S.L.

58

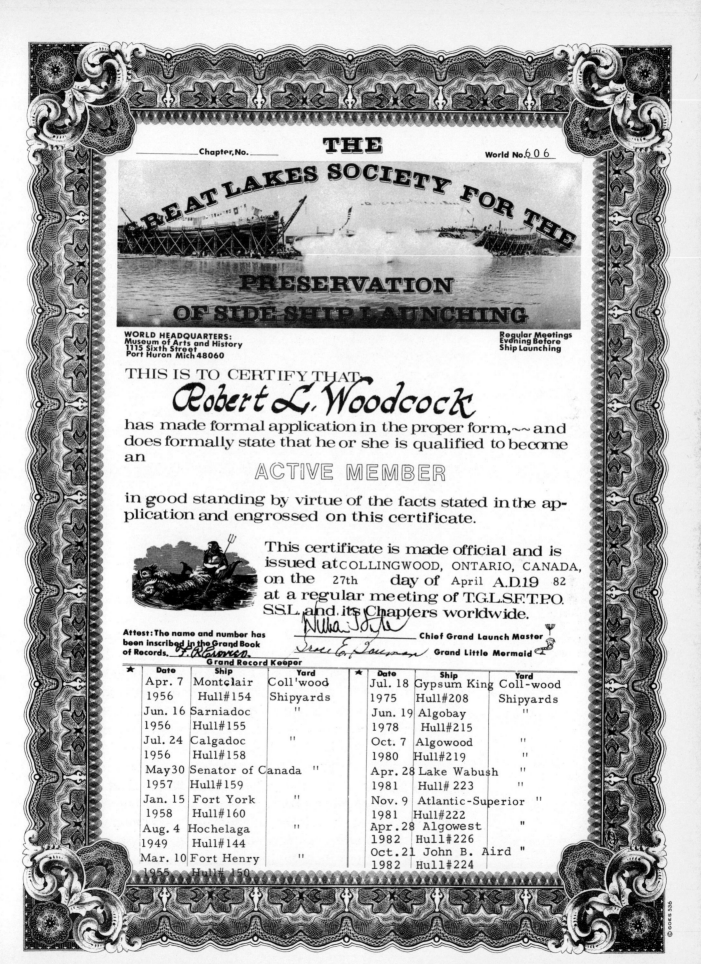

Chapter, No. _____

THE
GREAT LAKES SOCIETY FOR THE

World No. 606

PRESERVATION
OF SIDE SHIP LAUNCHING

WORLD HEADQUARTERS:
Museum of Arts and History
1115 Sixth Street
Port Huron Mich 48060

Regular Meetings
Evening Before
Ship Launching

THIS IS TO CERTIFY THAT

Robert L. Woodcock

has made formal application in the proper form, ~~ and does formally state that he or she is qualified to become an

ACTIVE MEMBER

in good standing by virtue of the facts stated in the application and engrossed on this certificate.

This certificate is made official and is issued at COLLINGWOOD, ONTARIO, CANADA, on the 27th day of April A.D.19 82 at a regular meeting of T.G.L.S.F.T.P.O. S.S.L. and its Chapters worldwide.

Attest: The name and number has been inscribed in the Grand Book of Records.

Grand Record Keeper

Chief Grand Launch Master

Grand Little Mermaid

★	Date	Ship	Yard	★	Date	Ship	Yard
	Apr. 7 1956	Montclair Hull#154	Coll'wood Shipyards		Jul. 18 1975	Gypsum King Hull#208	Coll-wood Shipyards
	Jun. 16 1956	Sarniadoc Hull#155	"		Jun. 19 1978	Algobay Hull#215	"
	Jul. 24 1956	Calgadoc Hull#158	"		Oct. 7 1980	Algowood Hull#219	"
	May 30 1957	Senator of Canada Hull#159	"		Apr. 28 1981	Lake Wabush Hull# 223	"
	Jan. 15 1958	Fort York Hull#160	"		Nov. 9 1981	Atlantic-Superior Hull#222	"
	Aug. 4 1949	Hochelaga Hull#144	"		Apr.28 1982	Algowest Hull#226	"
	Mar. 10 1955	Fort Henry Hull# 150	"		Oct.21 1982	John B. Aird Hull#224	"

© GOES 536

Superstructure of M/V JOHN B. AIRD rises above Collingwood's main street.

While there are isolated shipyards throughout the world which continue to side launch ships, the greater width of the launching basins at those locations eliminates the awesome engineering challenge present at Collingwood side-ship launches. When thousands of spectators participate in a midweek industrial event, which receives only nominal advance publicity, it becomes apparent that something unique is happening. It is not surprising therefore that the society has chosen Collingwood as the most sacred of ship launching locations.

On launch morning the society members quickly renew the enthusiasm experienced during their launch-eve meeting. They eagerly join the stream of other spectators heading toward the Collingwood Shipyards located at the foot of Collingwood's main street. From this viewpoint the drama of the side-launching spectacle begins to unfold immediately upon sighting the ship. The huge hull sits atop its building berth, towering above

the surrounding three and four-storey buildings. The effect is
even more awesome when the ship is constructed with the stern
facing the main street. Imagine a ten-storey structure sitting atop
a launch ramp at the end of the town's main street.

By launch day the vessel has been painted in its company's
colours, transforming it from a dull brownish mass of steel to a
gleaming and majestic figure. The ship's name is neatly painted
in white lettering on the port and starboard quarters of the forward and aft ends, but remains veiled by red, white and blue
banners until the christening ceremony is performed at the moment of launch.

A Canadian flag flies proudly from a mast located at the
highest point of the ship, about 115 feet above the ground. Other
forms of decorations adorn the vessel including the distinctive
Collship flag and the flag of the shipping company to which the
vessel will be registered.

Spectators seek highest possible vantage point, with media photographers on scaffolding, and even a cherry picker.

There are only two prime locations from which to view the launch. One is within the shipyard grounds. The other is an area located on a narrow spit of land which is accessed by a roadway running immediately adjacent to the east side of the shipyard. This roadway runs north toward the Collingwood grain elevator facility. The roadway also services the Collingwood Yacht Club and a public launching facility for small pleasure craft.

Many experienced side-launch fans insist that this spit of land is the ideal vantage point from which to view the launching. Judging from the large crowd which gathers at that meeting place for each launch, it is in fact a favorite location. For spectators who plan to view a launch from this area it is important to know that the roadway is closed at 11:00 a.m. on launch days.

62

This precaution is necessary because the wave of water created by the launching normally rushes over the roadway. Anyone standing in the wave's path would quickly become a fast moving body surfer.

By 10:30 a.m. on launch morning the core of seasoned spectators has gathered and becomes immersed in the drama of launch activity. For the next 45 minutes the pace of spectator arrivals intensifies and the late-comers can be seen jockeying for any remaining acceptable viewing locations.

In order to fully appreciate the drama of the pre-launch procedures it is necessary to arrive at the launch site early. Upon entering the shipyard a feeling of excitement takes hold and any presumption that the launch is a routine process has now been dispelled. The enormous size of the hull and massive array of launch equipment being handled by hundreds of shipyard workers is an overwhelming sight. A manned ambulance parked on site sobers one to the dangers involved, however, shipyard officials in charge appear calm and confident as they observe the preparation. But still, an underlying tenseness can be detected.

Collship supervisors observe launch preparation procedures.

They've engineered many perfect launches, but there have also been launches when even the most carefully calculated procedures have fallen prey to the elements of adverse weather conditions or equipment failure. These are infrequent and certainly not anticipated. But spectators often wonder, "Will this be a perfect launch or will there be problems?" The answer to that question is never known until the triggers fall to the ground and the ship is released on its journey into the launching basin.

Most spectators are in position well in advance of the normal 11:45 a.m. launch time, so there is considerable time for speculation and conversation. Strangers make friends easily as the unifying and mysterious bond which surrounds the side-launching spectacle captivates the imagination.

Razor sharp axe used for chopping through manila rope .

6

ACTION BENEATH THE SHIP

Launch morning is the final culmination of over 16,000 hours of preparation and testing. Safety is always a major consideration during the period of construction, but on launch morning safety becomes the number one priority. Before launch day preparations begin, the hundreds of workers involved with the launch are called together at the Launchmaster's platform for a thorough briefing. Launch procedures are reviewed, a chain of command is established and safety rules are clearly defined including an emergency plan for total evacuation of the launch area if deemed necessary by the Launchmaster. When the briefing is complete, the launch crew of about 350 workers disperses and begin their specific responsibilities at the launch site. Colour-coded jackets are worn by specific crew and crew leaders for the purpose of immediate visible identification by the Launchmaster and superintendents.

Tell-tale measuring device is calibrated on the morning of launch.

The 20 men designated as *axemen* each take charge of an axe which has been honed to the sharpness of a razor. In preparation for the *cut*, a wooden chopping block has been placed beneath each of the looping arrangements of manila rope which form the *soft link* in the 20 trigger restraining cable systems. Each chopping block is identified with the surname of the axeman responsible for that particular chopping location. He must remain in the vicinity of his designated chopping block and guard his axe while awaiting the Launchmaster's signal to cut.

A minimum of eight other men are assigned to man the hydraulic jacks, however like the axemen, their prime duty will not commence until near launch moment. Another eight workers, designated as *tell-tale men,* advance to three locations along the inboard side of the launch ramp. Three men are positioned at the bow, three at the stern and two amidships. At these three locations unique movement measuring devices have been installed to provide a positive means to monitor and record any sideways movment of the hull during the launch preparation process. The movement measuring devices known as *tell-tales* consist of two narrow strips of wood running together. The upper wand-like strip is secured to a butterboard and the other at-

66

Army of 220 men take hold of sledgehammers and move into position.

Several members of the launching gang gather near the bow of JOHN H.J. HAGARTY on June 18, 1914. Some of these same sledgehammers pictured here still remain in use today.

Each of 10,000 wedges must be driven between the ship and the launchway to lift it from the building berth.

tached to that butterboard's mating launchway. Any movement of the ship hull will cause the wand portion of the tell-tale device, which is painted bright red and marked with an indicator line, to move along a graduated measuring medium imprinted on the mating portion of the tell-tale which is attached to the stationary launchway.

While the 20 axemen, 8 jackmen, and 8 tell-tale men are taking up their positions, another 220 workers take charge of sledge hammers weighing 8 pounds each. Led by one rally leader and 10 gang leaders, they break up into 10 gangs and head for the ship's forward end where the first 10 launchways are located. Starting at the ship's bow and progressing through to launchway number 47, located at the ship's stern, the name of each gang leader has been inscribed at the top of each launchway. The 220 workers, with sledgehammers in hand, position themselves underneath the forward end of the ship hull.

The task which they are about to undertake would seem impossible. Remembering that 9000 tons of weight hang above their heads, the objective is to drive the 10,000 wooden wedges (which were installed earlier in the preparation process) into the packing timbers, between the ship's bottom and the launch-

68

ways, with sufficient force to lift the hull off the supports on which it was constructed. While only a small amount of lift is required to transfer the vessel's weight to the 47 launchways, it is necessary to make two complete passes along the launch ramp to attain the desired result. This function is performed in a highly organized manner through numerous wedge-driving sessions known as *rallies*. To attain the maximum amount of lifting force from each wooden wedge, all 220 sledgehammers must function in unison. To accomplish this the rally leader and ten gang leaders are equipped with conventional whistles similar to ones used for sporting events. When the rally leader is satisfied that his ten gang leaders and all workers are in position, he sounds a loud blast from his whistle as a signal to the gang leaders to give their whistle signals. In response, the 220 men grasp their sledge hammers and begin pounding in the 2000 wedges spaced along the full length of the ten launchways. Each rally continues for

Rally leader signals with his whistle for sledgehammers to begin the next rally.

69

Rally member takes a well deserved rest between exhausting sledgehammer rallies.

70

approximately one minute during which time the resounding clatter of sledgehammers impacting the wedges is audible throughout the entire town of Collingwood. It's a sound filled with intrigue and spurs one of the many emotional sensations experienced by side-launch spectators. The *driving-up* process continues, with the rally gangs leap-frogging in two groups of five along the 47 launchways, until they reach the hull's stern. After a short rest period, the same process is repeated starting at the stern and progressing back towards the bow. During this second pass along the launchways, the massive weight of the ship hull will be fully transferred from the construction supports to the launchways. This is a physically exhausting process which accounts for the rallies being fractured into intervals of about one minute each. The rally gangs are rewarded for their efforts by being given the afternoon off from work after the ship has been launched.

As the rally gangs make their second pass along the launchways a block removal *ram gang* of about 20 members follow behind. They must remove all shoring posts and keel blocking upon which the hull previously rested. Occasionally when adequate lift has not been attained during the driving-up process at a particular location of the vessel, the sound of a chain saw roars from beneath the hull indicating the need to sever a shoring post. Two members of the ram gang are armed with chain saws for that purpose. While it is desirable that the chain saws not be used, there are occasions when both saws will be heard simultaneously humming their way through shoring posts which cannot be removed in the conventional manner.

With the ship's weight now fully transferred to the 47 launch-ways, the only two restraining systems left holding the ship are the *dog cleats* and *trigger mechanisms*. It was at this point in the launch preparation process of TADOUSSAC (hull No. 192) on May 29, 1969 that the Collingwood Shipyards experienced its only serious mishap during a launching. On that tragic morning TADOUSSAC prematurely broke loose from her secured position atop the launch ramp and roared down the launchways while the 350-man launch crew scrambled in all directions, survival their only objective. With drag chains lashing the air in all directions and launch timber being tossed and crushed by the forces of the uncontrolled launch, disaster was inevitable. The worst fears of shipyard officials and spectators were realized. Assessment of damage and human injury began immediately, but because some of the workers ran panic stricken from the launch site, it was several hours before a full accounting was completed. Two lives had been lost and more than 40 workers injured, many seriously. Once the injured had been cared for, attention was focused on the cause of the mishap. It was learned that some of the wooden trigger levers (which are now made from a steel I-beam) located at the hull's stern had broken, causing an uncontrolled release of the vessel. Officials observing the tell-tale marker at the hull's bow realized that a serious situation was developing when they detected the vessel's bow moving up the launchways as a result of the stern sliding down toward the launching basin. But there was no time to sound an alarm; disaster was already in progress.

For the men working on the top side of the launch ramp there were a few precious moments available for escape. But for all others beneath the vessel their only chance for survival was to find refuge among the crumbling timber.

As part of the Launchmaster's current launch morning briefing session, clear and explicit evacuation instructions are issued. Three portable horns are connected to a panic button located at the Launchmaster's platform and are operated independent of the shipyard's power system which is shut off just prior to launch. At the first indication of danger to the launch crew the Launchmaster will activate the horns. This is a specific signal for the entire launch crew to evacuate the launch site by running in a straight path between and parallel to the drag chains.

The tragic launch of TADOUSSAC. It began as a normal launch with the hull sitting quietly atop the launchway (top). In the middle photo, TADOUSSAC breaks loose from her secured position and begins an uncontrolled slide down the launchways with workers still underneath. The aftermath. Workers running in to help the more than 40 injured workers trapped in the launch debris.

Present day restraining devices have restored the confidence of the crew working underneath the ship.

Members of the launch crew who are required to perform tasks beneath the vessels are conscious of the dangers which they face. However, a flawless record since that disaster in 1969 has fully restored their confidence in the launch procedures currently followed by the Collingwood Shipyards. Officials take no chances when planning or executing a launching and, if there is even the slightest degree of doubt when making a decision, the safest alternative is always chosen.

When the rally gangs and ram gangs have completed their procedures just prior to launch time, all but about 120 workers leave the immediate launch site area and join the spectators who

have secured most of the areas authorized for viewing the launch. But, having spent the entire morning toiling beneath the ship, the workers want, and quietly demand, a clear view of the launch which will occur soon. They scramble atop any unoccupied structure, and for the next few minutes, its their shipyard and their ship as pride radiates from their beaming faces.

The workers remaining in the immediate vicinity of the launch site will perform the final three routines which will send the ship racing down the launchways. With only 15 minutes until launch time, the 12-man crew of *riggers* and *chippers* who will ride the ship into the launching basin prepare themselves for one of the

Just prior to launch only the essential launch crew remains on site.

75

Part of the 12-man crew of riggers and chippers prepare for the short but dramatic ride into the launch basin.

most thrilling experiences available to man. Until the launch of JOHN B. AIRD on October 21, 1982 it was extremely rare for anyone other than specific Collingwood Shipyard workers to remain aboard ship during a launch. However, because that ship hull was to be named in honour of John B. Aird, Lieutenant Governor of Ontario, a knowledgeable side ship launch enthusiast, special concessions were made. Fifteen minutes before launch time he was lifted aboard the waiting vessel in a special box known as the *bucket* which is transported by crane. Accompanying Aird was William Davis, Premier of Ontario, Collingwood Shipyard officials and representatives of Algoma Central Railway, the company for which the ship was being built. Adding to the abnormally large number of people riding the hull

76

On board JOHN B. AIRD, William Davis (on right), Premier of Ontario, walks with John B. Aird, Lieutenant Governor of Ontario.

At the launch of JOHN B. AIRD party of dignitaries are hoisted aboard ship by crane (left). In the bottom photo, William Davis (centre) and John B. Aird on his left, take position with shipyard officials.

Dale Green, guest of television show "Thrill of a Lifetime", gets strapped into position by Joe Sheffer (right), and George Low of Collingwood Shipyards.

were a number of the news media, and a film crew from the television show "Thrill of a Lifetime". The production crew members unanimously agreed that the side-launching of JOHN B. AIRD was the most thrilling happening recorded during their several years of producing shows based on thrilling experiences. The ultimate compliment had been paid to Collingwood's side-launch spectacle.

At ground level just prior to launch, the spectators sense that the moment they have been waiting for is about to happen. Two men with sledgehammers in hand can be seen at the top end of each launchway awaiting the Launchmaster's signal to "remove the dogs". When the Launchmaster finally shouts his command the waiting men each drive two pre-installed wedges between the dogs and mating launchways to pop the dogs loose. Because of the limited space between the hull bottom and the launchways the men have little space in which to swing the hammers. Normally the dogs are removed after one or two sledgehammer blows, but there are occasions when a wedge will require many blows. The ensuing delay adds to the tension already prevelant among the spectators.

80

At the launching of JOHN B. AIRD, the worker assigned to remove the outward-facing dog on the launchway at the extreme southern end of the launch ramp experienced difficulty doing so. Though irritated at his predicament, a more sobering thought was on his mind; "Will this ship start moving down the launch ramp while I'm beneath it"? He is aware that once the dogs have been removed only 20 triggers remain in place to hold the massive hull in a controlled position. Movement of the ship at that moment of the launch process is highly unlikely, but he's not receptive to calculating the odds while standing alone beneath an anxious mountain of steel. His objective is to get the dog removed and then depart the scene and join his counterparts who have already moved quickly away from the launch site.

One of the 94 dog cleats used to help hold the vessel into position.

Jackmen activate the hydraulic jacks pressing against the inboard bilge line of the hull.

When all the dog cleats have been removed the entire area beneath the ship hull is carefully searched by four superintendents to ensure no obstructions remain above the plane of the launchways. More importantly, they also satisfy themselves that no workers remain beneath the ship. They then report to the Launchmaster that "all is clear". The Launchmaster then instructs the *jackmen* to activate their hydraulic jacks which are pressing against the inboard bilge line of the hull. Their objective is to create a *live ship* by breaking any initial friction between the butterboards and launchways which have been compressed together for several weeks.

Normally some sideways movement of the vessel has already taken place during the driving-up process and this has required the jackmen to activate their jacks slightly in order to keep the jacks pressurized against the ship hull. When movement is

82

detected on the tell-tale devices located at the forward or aft ends of the vessel it is recorded on large tell-tale signal boards. The information on the boards is visible to the Launchmaster, and as well he receives reports by radio from the tell-tale teams to confirm movement recorded on the boards. Any movement at the amidships tell-tale location is recorded directly on the hull by use of a soap stone. This can also be seen by the Launchmaster from his platform located half-way along the launch site facing the inboard side of the launch ramp.

Final jack pressure is applied until the hull has been moved about 3/4 of an inch down the launchways; this indicates that they have a *live ship*. The 20 triggers are now taut and ready to *fire* the huge ship into the water at the command of the Launchmaster.

Signal boards indicate that vessel has moved 3/16 inch down the launchway during the jacking process.

7

THE TIMBERS ROAR

With only the 20 triggers holding the ship onto the launchways, the major portion of the launch preparation has now been completed. The 20 axemen stand poised along the inboard side of the towering vessel knowing that once they cut the manila ropes to release the triggers they must speedily depart between the huge drag chains.

At the ship's bow the official party representing government officials, senior executives of the Collingwood Shipyards, representatives of the company purchasing the ship, and the sponsor who will christen the ship are all gathered on a platform decorated in red, white and blue bunting.

Traditionally, the wife of an executive member from the purchasing company is extended the highly honoured privilege of performing the *christening* immediately following the *blessing* of the ship by the minister. Considering the nature of both the blessing and christening of a ship one would expect both functions to be uneventful. But like all aspects of a side-launch

The timbers roar during the launch of JOHN B. AIRD. Cover painting by Martin (Ted) Visser.

85

Royal Canadian Legion Pipe Band performs during launch ceremonies of PRAIRIE HARVEST.

nothing can be taken for granted. At the launching of BLACK BAY on September 20, 1962, the Priest, Father Bauer, conducted the blessing ceremony in English as usual. However, then he decided to repeat the blessing in Latin. Meanwhile beneath the ship, timbers were creaking and groaning from the strain of the ship's weight on the restraining triggers. Shipyard officials knowing the signs of an anxious ship became very anxious themselves as they waited for the first opportunity to cut the 730-foot ship loose when the extended blessing was finally completed.

Complications with the blessing ceremonies maybe, but what could possibly go wrong with the christening function? Surely the task of smashing a small bottle of champagne against a huge steel hull should present no difficulties. So thought Mrs. G.E. MacKinnon who, representing Shell Canadian Tankers Limited, had the pleasure of christening TYEE SHELL on July 23, 1958. Mrs. MacKinnon had never before experienced a side ship launching and not having been informed that TYEE SHELL would be side-launched, understandably assumed that

86

the ship would quietly launch stern-first into the harbour in the more conventional manner. Champagne bottle in hand, and standing before the public address microphone, she proudly conducted the christening speech and then eagerly smashed the decorated bottle of champagne against the vessel. At first pleased with herself, she then became startled and confused as the ship creaked and groaned while moving sideways down the launchways. Concerned that she had somehow created a catastrophe Mrs. MacKinnon shouted aloud, with the open microphone still before her, "Oh my God, what have I done"? Once the ship stabilized she was relieved to learn that the intended path of TYEE SHELL was in fact sideways down the launch-ramp and the catastrophe which she had just created was a routine launch.

Launch of TYEE SHELL on July 23, 1958.

87

The christening ceremony ends with champagne bottle exploding against the ship's bow.

On another occasion, at the launching of Algoma Marines's ALGOWOOD on October 7, 1980, Mrs. Douglas A. Berlis, representing Algoma Central Railway of Sault Ste. Marie, Ontario also underestimated the potential challenges of christening a ship. On cue from shipyard officials she thrust the champagne bottle, which was dangling from the end of a colourful lanyard, against ALGOWOOD's bow expecting the bottle to smash into fragments. But something went wrong! The bottle struck the ship, an echo rang throughout the shipyard, but the bottle didn't break. When the bottle, still intact, bounced back to her she grasped it once again, determined to make the foam flow from it this time. But it was not to be! As she thrust the bottle toward the ship it fell from the lanyard, struck the ground and exploded. The launch took place but ALGOWOOD had to wait until after launch, and lunch, for her christening. In the early afternoon another bottle of champagne was attached to the lanyard and Mrs. Berlis announced that she would, "do this until I get it right", which she did.

An ideal christening results when the champagne bottle explodes against the bow at the same moment the Launchmaster signals to launch the ship. At this moment the hull has officially

Launchmaster Fred McAr-thur raises red signal board above his head to signal axe-men to prepare to "cut".

been transferred to the status of *ship*. Confirmation of that fact is provided when the workers aboard ship unveil the ship's name by raising the bunting shrouds at launch moment.

Also at that moment, down on the launchways, the eyes of all 20 axemen are focused on the Launchmaster as he raises a red two-foot square board above his head while standing on his rais-ed platform. The spectators become tense, cameras are held at the ready. The sight of 20 axes being held high in the air means the scene is about to explode with an awesome array of activity.

Signal board held above his head, the Launchmaster takes one last look to the foward and aft ends of the ship. Once he has scanned the launch site for the last time before the launch he must make the decision to cut the ship loose. He knows that when a commitment to *cut* is made there is no turning back. The 16,000 hours of launch preparation time will be put to the ultimate test during the next 10 seconds. There are no rehearsals and there's no second chance. When he decides, "yes, I'm ready," he swings his red signal board down in a rapid motion giving the command to the axemen to cut. The 20 axemen simultaneously chop through the trigger restraining loops of manila rope lying stretched atop the chopping blocks. Then they immediately depart the scene, axes in hand, as the Launch-master sounds the emergency horns — more as a symbolic gesture than a necessity. The 20 trigger devices release with a re-sounding clang as they fall to the ground, free of the enormous force which had held them in place under tension. The ship is now released to the force of gravity and should immediately commence travelling sideways down the 47 lubricated launch-ways.

Axemen chop through the restraining triggers (top), and then proceed to depart the scene as the ship begins its slide.

89

While immediate movement of the ship is desirable and probable, there have been instances when ships have *hung-up* on the launch ramp. Such hang-ups can result from minor imperfections in a launch plan. Delicate balances enter into the process of side-launching large vessels. Declivity of the launchways must be sufficient to force the ship to move, but not too steep because of Collingwood's narrow basin. Jacking pressure must be adequate to reduce the friction existing between the launchways and butterboards, however there are limitations to the number of triggers which can be used and the restraining capacity of each trigger during the jacking process. The mixture of lubricants must be of ideal texture to retain coherence with the timber, and yet be slippery enough to minimize friction.

To all of these conflicting requirements add the fickle Canadian weather conditions, and it becomes obvious why complica-

tions can arise. One of the most dramatic hang-ups in recent years occured on October 7, 1980 when ALGOWOOD sat atop the launch ramp for 14 minutes, stubbornly resisting her launch after the triggers snapped free. Any hang-up of this kind creates tense moments for the Launchmaster. He must decide if the jackmen will be required to return to the ship's side and reactivate the hydraulic jacks. Not an eviable assignment for the jackmen. When a hang-up occurs there is also the frightening possibility of an uneven launch resulting from either the forward or aft end of the ship moving uncontrolled in advance of the ship's opposite end. This did happen to ALGOWOOD when she eventually slid down the launchways in a transverse fashion with the forward end leading the stern by about 30 feet. PRAIRIE HARVEST reacted in the very same manner during her launching on October 18, 1983.

During a hangup jackmen return to reactivate a hydraulic jack in the launch of PRAIRIE HARVEST, and in bottom photo two of launch crew watch for movement at the forward end of the launch ramp.

In an example of an uneven launch, PRAIRIE HAR-VEST moves down the launchways with the bow end leading the stern.

A nearly identical situation appeared to be developing while launching JOHN B. AIRD, however not to the extremes which occured during the launches of ALGOWOOD and PRAIRIE HARVEST. JOHN B. AIRD was the 13th vessel launched under the direction of Launchmaster Fred McArthur, but no amount of experience could dispel his sense of anxiety over a possible hang-up in the launch.

One such hang-up, causing extreme transverse movement during a launch occured during the launching of the steamer NEVADA at Manitowoc, Wisconsin in 1915. When the Launchmaster gave his signal for the axemen to cut, the axeman positioned at the bow trigger chop block swung at the rope with his axe but missed. He made another attempt to cut the rope but missed again. Another worker saw the problem and retrieved the axe which had become imbedded in the chop block. He then cut the forward trigger loose, but not before NEVADA's stern

Considerable damage occurred to the steamer NEVADA when the stern end of the vessel was launched ahead of the bow at Manitowoc, Wisconsin.

93

Launch of ATLANTIC SUPERIOR on November 9, 1981. A series of 6 sequence photographs shows the action.

PRAIRIE HARVEST rages toward the far wall of the launching basin just before being snapped back by the drag chains.

had already moved several feet into the water. Considerable damage occured to NEVADA's hull as a result of the vessel's stern dropping off the launch ramp while the bow was still secured in position.

Another example of a possible mishap occured at Collingwood on January 12, 1959. That side-launch was, as usual, attended by several officials representing the company purchasing the ship about to be launched. They were receiving an ex-

planation of the launch process from the late W.A. Alex
Webster. Mr. Webster, then General Manager of Collingwood
Shipyards, confidently informed the party of officials that
MENIHEK LAKE would "leap into the water when the triggers
snap free." The cold weather of that day would soon
demonstrate the difficulty of predicting the launch action. As
the axemen sliced through the manila ropes restraining
MENIHEK LAKE they ran from the unrestrained ship, but it

sat *frozen* to the launchways, without a trace of movement evident. The jackmen who had joined the spectators were summoned back to persuade the ship to "leap" into the water. After a few moments MENIHEK LAKE rumbled down the launch ramp to the relief of Mr. Webster as a cheer rose from the crowd.

When all equipment operates perfectly, calculations by the design department prove exact, and weather conditions are favourable, the ship does in fact seem to leap toward the water. The first few inches of movement comes slowly, but then as the massive weight of the ship takes over, the ship accelerates rapidly. It roars down the launchways in a terrifying rush like an uncontrolled avalanche as timbers groan and snap under the enormous strain and pressure exerted on them. The thunderous noise, created by 500,000 board-feet of timber snapping and breaking, echoes off the surrounding buildings and can be heard throughout the town. Spectators stand in a state of awe as they watch in disbelief, thinking "this is incredible, that ship is out of control." Not out of control, but a kind of controlled explosion.

As the ship travels down the launch ramp it becomes progressively suspended over the launching basin. This causes the massive array of packing timber to begin tumbling into the water like 47 rows of collapsing cordwood falling from beneath the ship. When the ship's centerline approaches the launchway's endpoint, its entire weight is carried on the inboard side of the hull, exerting tremendous pressures on the launch timbers underneath. This extreme pressure lasts only a moment though, as the ship heels over and plunges off the launch ramp into the water. A huge wave of water is created along the ship's entire outboard side.

On the inboard side of the launch ramp another scene of explosive action is unfolding. For the first several feet of its launch the ship moves unrestrained down the launchways. Then at a precisely calculated point, 11 of the 18 drag chains begin loosening their slack and start dragging their respective drag boxes along the prepared trenches. This core of drag boxes begin checking the ship's thrust as they travel a distance of about 12 feet at which point the remaining chains and drag boxes become effective as well. All 18 drag boxes, with a combined weight of over 600 tons, simultaneously travel for about 4 feet where they plough into the earth. The huge chains lash about in the air threatening anything in their path. This action brings the upper plane of the 9000 ton ship to an immediate stop at a point 18 in-

Launch sequence of PRAIRIE HARVEST as seen from an inboard-side vantage point. Note the whipsawing action of the 18 huge drag chains.

ALGOWEST (above) and ALGOPORT (opposite page) plunge into the water and within inches of the east wall of the launch basin.

ches past the centre line of the launching basin. The bottom of the ship then thrusts toward the far wall of the launching basin where its bilge line comes within only a few feet of striking it. This is a frightening sight for the novice side-launch spectator who imagines the ship roaring out of control, and then watches as the mountain of steel instantly stops like a raging bull caught in a steel net. A cheer goes up from the crowd and the air is filled with elation and gaiety as water floods in all directions. Wet feet become the standard reception for spectators viewing the launch from within the shipyard at ground level.

Wet feet become the standard reception for spectators viewing the launch from ground level in the shipyard.

There can also be unpleasant surprises of a more serious nature. During the launching of JOHN B. AIRD two shipyard workers who were standing in a normally safe location were tossed to the ground by a rushing wake of water flowing throughout the launch ramp. Scrambling like drowning rats, they finally regained their footing in time to keep from being swept into the raging water of the launching basin.

Replacing the massive amount of water displaced from the launching basin is water rushing in from the harbour. To prevent the force of the replacement water from pushing the ship into the head end of the launching basin's concrete wall, a huge cable leads across the harbour where it is secured to a compressor-type winch which is firmly bolted to a concrete pier. The cable is drawn taut by the winch at the moment the Launch-

102

master gives his command to the axemen to cut the ship loose. The critical instruction to *cut* is broadcast over walkie-talkie equipment held by the various key launch workers, including those who operate the winch. The importance of this cable restraining system was clearly demonstrated on November 6, 1981.

On that cold November morning, hull No. 222 ATLANTIC SUPERIOR was scheduled to strike the water of Collingwood at 11:45 a.m. But high winds gusting to over 50 miles per hour from the northwest was creating havoc with the forward end of the hull. If ATLANTIC SUPERIOR had been a finished vessel at the time of her launch the launch could probably have been completed as planned. However, only the 600-foot aft portion of the vessel had been constructed at Collingwood, while the

The winch cable is drawn taut as it holds ALGOPORT from backing into the launch basin.

103

130-foot forward section was built at the Portship division in Thunder Bay, Ontario. As a result, the half-hull was blunt at the forward end. This shape caused strong wind resistance against the hull, heightening the chances of damage in the event of a restraining cable or winch failure. When the winds refused to calm, the launch was aborted at 10:30 a.m., at a time when the driving-up process had been about half completed. That instance represented the only time the Collingwood Shipyards has ever aborted a launch once final preparations had commenced. However, considering the exceptional circumstances prevailing on that day, the decision to postpone the launch until November 9, 1981 was prudent. It clearly demonstrates the care and respect for safety taken by the shipyard officials during a launch.

The postponement of that launch did of course cause considerable disappointment and inconvenience to the thousands of spectators who had travelled to Collingwood to witness what was scheduled to be the most spectacular side ship launch ever performed because of the record weight of hull No. 222. That hull was the first self-unloader ship constructed by Collingwood Shipyards to ocean-going specifications. To knowledgeable spectators who were aware of this fact, the postponement was particularly disappointing. But, like all of life's setbacks, there was a bright side to help offset the disappointment. This unprecedented rescheduling of a side-launching at Collingwood presented an ideal opportunity to determine the true magnetism of the spectacle. Would many spectators take another day off work by rescheduling their "case of the flu", or would they forgo the excitement of this launch? As it turned out, not only did they return, but news reports of the aborted launching resulted in the largest crowd ever to attend a side-launching at Collingwood. Over 15,000 spectators were definitely not disappointed this time. The launch lived up to its billing and provided spectacular entertainment when ATLANTIC SUPERIOR finally thundered into the launch basin.

The main flood of water created during launching extends along the full length of the ship. An enormous volume of water flows over the east basin wall and rushes along the ground until it strikes a wave deflector, resembling a mammoth snow-plow blade, positioned alongside of a three-storey building. A tremendous thrust is generated by the wall of raging water which is forced upward as it crashes against the wave deflector. The water reaches a height of over 50 feet before it plunges back to the ground.

Wave deflector at Collingwood Shipyards is mounted against a building adjacent to the launching basin.

At the outward end of the launching basin there are no immediate obstructions to the wave. It travels for several hundred feet across the harbour, and finally when it reaches the narrow spit of land leading to the location used by spectators to view launchings, it smashes against a concrete dock and spews across the roadway. At the launching of ATLANTIC SUPERIOR the wave roared across the roadway toward Constable Gregory Brindisi of the Collingwood Police Force, who was conducting traffic and crowd control in what was traditionally a safe location. However, ATLANTIC SUPERIOR was about to break all

A huge wave is forced up-ward by the wave deflector during the launch of ATLANTIC SUPERIOR.

previous records for displacement of water by flooding land to an extent never before experienced at a Collingwood side ship launching. The ground beneath Constable Brindisi became one of those areas as the flood of water washed in and knocked him off his feet. He was not injured, however a portable radio on his belt was water damaged and required repair. Many spectators unfamiliar with Collingwood launchings fail to appreciate the need for crowd control. Incidents like the one on that cold day in November 1981 leave no doubt that the unexpected can easily happen during any launching.

8

CAN I SEE THAT AGAIN?

When the launched ship begins to stabilize in the launching basin, the thousands of thrilled spectators remain excited as they scan the launch scene which is now in total disarray. In the space of ten seconds they have watched the launch area transformed from a neat and orderly setting to a mass of crushed and scrambled timber. Muddy water saturates the ground and fish splash about in the large puddles, later to be tossed by shipyard workers back into the launching basin.

The enormous task which seemed impossible only moments earlier has now been successfully accomplished. The huge towering mass of steel has been dramatically transferred sideways from a location several feet above ground level to the small basin of water without any apparent damage to the vessel. Shipyard officials, especially the Launchmaster, beam with pride in recognition of their successful accomplishment like a mother who has just given birth to her child.

The spectators, including numerous media crews, slowly descend from their viewing positions and file past the ship and launch ramp in a state of amazement. The Honourable John B. Aird, Lieutenant Governor of Ontario, has attended several side ship launchings at Collingwood and says; "It's marvelous, very exciting, like the creation of a new being." Larry Beaton of Ottawa, Ontario who required several days of coaxing to attend his first side-launching, offered a brief but vivid description of a launch. He said, "incredible, just incredible; it just doesn't seem possible." Mrs. Douglas A. Berlis, who is associated with Algoma Central Marine, represents one of several thousand women who also enjoy the spectacle. Mrs. Berlis eloquently described the side-launching of ALGOWOOD on October 7, 1980: "There can be few more exciting experiences in this life than that of watching a great new vessel move first very slowly, then with a terrifying rush from dry land into its natural habitat in the water."

And how would a professional illustrator describe a side ship launching? Marten "Ted" Visser, an artist from Craigleith, Ontario witnessed a side-launching for the first time on October 21, 1982 when, after much persuading by his son Marten Jr., he reluctantly agreed to see JOHN B. AIRD launched. Arriving 90 minutes in advance of launch moment and standing in a large crowd on a day when high winds and freezing temperatures prevailed was no treat for someone who was "dragged" to the site. But he soon became intrigued by the pre-launch procedures, sensing that the long cold wait for launch moment would not be without reward. While viewing the towering ship and the small narrow basin, he began to doubt that the ship could be safely launched; a common thought to first-time spectators. After the launch was safely executed Ted was quick to admit that there was far too much action taking place in that ten-second flash of time to be appreciated during the viewing of only one launch. He was so moved by his exposure to the launching of JOHN B. AIRD that he chose to relive the experience by producing the outstanding oil painting which adorns the cover of this book. His overall assessment of the spectacle was, "unbelievable, far more spectacular that I ever expected. I'd like to see it over again." That insightfull observation describes the feelings of most spectators; there is too much action to absorb in only one viewing, and the impact far exceeds one's expectations.

As the excitement of the launch begins to subside, a series of post-launch routines begins, and when completed will take 2000 man-hours, bringing the total number of launch related man hours to 18,000. The crew designated to ride the ship into the launching basin inagurates the post-launch routines by undertaking an inspection of the ship's structure to determine and record any apparent damage caused during its launch.

On the afternoon following each launching, several dignitaries representing the purchasing company, officials of the Collingwood Shipyards and other invited guests attend a luncheon hosted by the shipyard. As part of the luncheon ceremonies, the christening sponsor is presented with a commemorative gift for her historically high profile function of christening the ship. Owners of the newly created ship typically compliment the shipyard for producing such a fine product. Shipyard management in turn is always quick to acknowledge the important role played by each of their nearly 1000 workers by stating; "It's their collective conscientious effort which makes Collingwood Shipyards a leader in the Canadian shipbuilding industry."

500,000 board feet of timber becomes a scrambled mess in 10 short seconds.

Launching timbers are restacked and await the next launch.

Also during the afternoon of each launch day a major post-launch task commences. The 500,000 board-feet of launch timber that has been scattered in all directions by the vessel during launch must be recovered. All packing timbers and the butterboards, totaling about 250,000 board-feet, which was carried down the launchways with the ship, lies floating in the launching basin or has been trapped beneath the ship. To retrieve the timber beneath the ship its bottom is swept with a special piece of launchway, which is dragged from one side of the ship to the other for its entire length. After retrieving all of the timber, the lubricants are scraped from the launchways and butterboards. The lubricants cannot be reused as the base and slip coats have been blended together under pressure during the launch. A large quantity of the timber is either crushed, splintered or cracked during the launch and becomes scrap. All undamaged and reusable timber is sorted and carefully piled in a manner which facilitates drying, and will be reused for the next launching.

For convenience and access to services and supplies during outfitting, the vessel is positioned in the launching basin with its stern, where the bulk of a ship's components are located, at the basin's south end. Except for the rare occasion when a ship is launched with its stern facing the south end of the basin, it is necessary to tow it out into the harbour and reverse its position

112

For 5 months after her launch, PRAIRIE HAR-VEST spent the winter of 1983-84 at Collingwood being outfitted.

113

*NANTICOKE leaves Coll-
ingwood on June 12, 1980
and passes her sea trials on
Georgian Bay.*

in the basin. The ship will remain in that position for a period of about 5 months while the thousands of detailed outfitting tasks are completed by the various technical and finishing tradesmen. During this time the ship becomes part of the town's landscape as its superstructure towers above the adjacent two and three-storey buildings at the end of main street.

About two weeks from completion the ship is moved to the outer end of the town docks. At its new location the water is deep enough to allow activation of the vessel's propulsion

114

system while being firmly secured to the dock during a series of testing routines known as *dock trials*. At that point the ship has reached its peak of magnificence and colourful beauty. The entire hull, including the superstructure, gleams with contrasting colours of deep blue and white, or red and white, the predominate colours for most of the ships constructed at Collingwood. The day to conduct the sea trials is chosen and if all tests prove positive, the ship commences its maiden voyage to take on the first of many loads of cargo to be transported by the vessel.

Because of its shallow depth, Collingwood harbour will never again see many of the ships built there. Six years after her launch, the 730 foot LOUIS R. DESMARAIS passes through Welland Canal, Ontario.

Due to the shallow draught of the Collingwood harbour the ship will most likely never return to the site where it was carefully built and proudly displayed during the final weeks before being put into service. But the ships built at Collingwood carry a unique birthmark which makes them readily identifiable as a Collingwood-built product. The inboard launch-side bears minor scars caused when the drag chain lugs are removed by a flame cutter after launch. As the eye scans along the side of a Collingwood-built ship the lug marks confirm its birthplace. The lug marks mean side-launch, and that means Collingwood Shipyards.

Meanwhile, back at the shipyards another massive ship hull is nearing completion while sitting atop the building berth. It has been nearly 5 months since the previous launch and the hull now forming on the building berth begins receiving considerable attention as shipyard workers prepare for its launch. For several weeks prior to a launch spectators can be seen diligently observing the launch scene as they drive, walk or boat within viewing

116

distance of the hull. They vividly recall the thrill and excitement experienced at past launches and begin to formulate plans to ensure their attendance on the next launch day. Telephone calls flow into the Collingwood Shipyards and the Chamber of Commerce requesting information on the date of the next launching. This date is tentative and is only confirmed about one month prior to launch day. For groups like T.G.L.S.F.T.P.O.S.S.L., and out-of-town school classes who wish to attend the side-launch, careful and flexible planning is required. For various reasons scheduled launch dates have been cancelled and rescheduled. This happens infrequently however, but it must be allowed for in a spectator's "launch plan".

The most effective way of keeping abreast of ongoing progress and the launch date of each ship hull is to subscribe to one of Collingwood's local weekly newspapers. One in particular, the Enterprise-Bulletin, "Home Newspaper of the Famous Blue Mountain Area", does an excellent job of reporting and photographing ongoing activities at Collingwood Shipyards.

As well, the Collingwood Chamber of Commerce is always pleased to respond to specific enquiries related to launch dates or general requests for information about Collingwood and the Collingwood Shipyards.

Gwynneth Cunningham (left) and Marjorie Rambo, both of Rexdale, Ontario are two side-launch enthusiasts who return for each launching at Collingwood. They're seen here among their growing collection of side-launch momentos.

Boaters in Collingwood harbour are among the many spectators viewing the progress of ships under construction.

Whether you obtain information about the spectacular side-launchings by newspaper, telephone or word-of-mouth, don't deprive yourself of one of life's most captivating experiences. You will become trapped by that unexplained compelling force which draws thousands of spectators back to the launch site to witness each successive launch. The ultimate goal is to have the launches performed on the weekend. Imagine an all-day festival centered around a noontime spectacular side-launching. I can hardly wait! And don't forget your camera so you can relive the spectacle while waiting to return for your second and subsequent side-launchings. Ask any one of the thousands of other side-launch enthusiasts if one launch satisfies their curiosity. They'll answer by returning to witness "Canada's Spectacular Avalanche of Steel" again and again.

118

Photo Credits

Back Cover Photography: Rob McEwan, System One, Toronto
Bay Shipbuilding Corp. Sturgeon Bay, Wisconsin 22

Courtesy of Collingwood Museum 26, 65

Harland & Wolff Shipyards Belfast, Northern Ireland 15-16
Reg Hewson 14
J. Albin Jackman 49
Wayne Parrar Niagara Falls, Ontario   Foreword
Port Weller Dry Docks St. Catharines, Ontario 13
Fritz Schuller Schuller Fotography, Collingwood, Ontario
 10, 25, 29, 30, 32-34, 50, 51, 73, 88, 94-95, 102-103, 114

Bernice Scotney 51

Shell Canada, Marine Division 92-93

All other photographs courtesy of:
Collingwood Enterprise-Bulletin Collingwood, Ontario
Christopher Woodcock
Robert Woodcock

About the Artist

Although well known to many private collectors, we introduce this gifted realist to our readers. Born in 1940 in Amsterdam, Holland, and now residing in Ontario, Marten Visser is an artist of great sensitivity and talent. He began his career as a magazine and book illustrator while maintaining his primary interest of painting. Visser has illustrated many books, most recently the re-published Hugh Garner series. Following the launching of JOHN B. AIRD, which he found extremely exciting, Visser volunteered to execute a painting for the book. The result is the inspiring work on our cover done in casein on a masonite panel.

A limited edition of 400 prints signed and numbered by the artist of the original painting will be issued and be locally available in Collingwood. Please direct all inquiries to: Marten Visser Studios, R.R. No. 3, Collingwood, Ontario L9Y 3Z2.